ORSON CART

and

THE HAUNTING OF HEADSTONE HALL

ORSON CART

and

THE HAUNTING OF HEADSTONE HALL

Steve Donald

RED FOX

To Soo, in loving memory

RED FOX

A Red Fox Book
Published by Random House Children's Books
20 Vauxhall Bridge Road, London SW1V 2SA

A division of Random House UK Ltd.
London Melbourne Sydney Auckland
Johannesburg and agencies throughout the world

First published by Hutchinson Children's Books 1994

Red Fox edition 1994

Printed and bound in Great Britain
by Cox & Wyman Ltd, Reading

RANDOM HOUSE UK Limited Reg. No. 954009

ISBN 0 09 916291 1

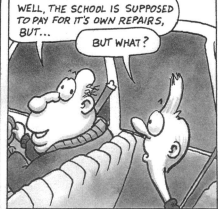

ARE THEY EVER GOING TO GO IN?
ARE THEY EVER GOING TO COME OUT AGAIN?
ARE THEY STUPID OR WHAT?

FIND OUT IN—

BLIMEY!
IT'S HUGE!

THAT'S OUR
UNCLE CEDRIC.

HE WAS A TERRIBLE MISER IN HIS
OLD AGE. HE WOULDN'T EVEN HAVE
A FIRE LIT IN THE HOUSE, THOUGH HE
OWNED ALL THE COAL FOR MILES AROUND!

HMM. A DEAD END. JUST THIS OLD CHAIN. I WONDER...

PUL

CLICK!

I DIDN'T MEAN TO SCARE ANYBODY *THAT* MUCH!

LADY HEADSTONE!

AGAIN!

THAT'S ME! JUST DOING MY BIT FOR CHARITY, YOU KNOW. HEARD ABOUT THE SPONSORSHIP PLAN. KNEW YOU'D NEED GHOSTS, BUT THE HOUSE DOESN'T HAVE ANY— —SO I CAME TO HELP OUT.

AH, I SEE MY BROTHER'S ALL RIGHT.

WELL, IT WOULD SERVE HIM RIGHT IF HE'D BROKEN HIS NECK! HE TRIED TO KILL US, AND HE'S GOING TO HELP LOADS OF PEOPLE ESCAPE FROM JAIL!

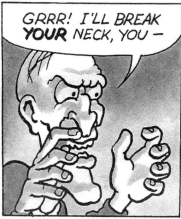